# Why Cats Hunt at Night

## Claire Llewellyn
### Illustrated by Simona Dimitri

RIGBY

Once upon a time, there was a cat.
Cat hunted in the day.
She hunted mice, birds and frogs.

At night, Cat went to sleep.

Cat wasn't very good at hunting in the day. The mice, birds and frogs could see her. "We can see you, Cat!" said the mice in the grass.

"We can see you!" said the birds up in the trees.
"Cat, we can see you!" said the frogs by the pond.
And the mice and the birds and the frogs always got away.

5

Poor Cat was always hungry.
Soon she was very, very tired.
One day, she was too tired to hunt.

Cat went to sleep and slept all day.
When she woke up, it was night.

Cat had not been out at night before.
How dark the night was!
How big and shiny the moon was!
How silver the moon made the pond!

Cat was still tired.
She went to the silver pond.
She washed her face.
Then she washed her eyes.

And what could Cat see with her big, shiny eyes?
She could see the mice in the grass.

She could see the birds up in the trees.
She could see the frogs by the pond.
But **they** could not see **her**!

Cat hunted all night.
She hunted mice, birds and frogs.

Soon it was day.

Cat was tired, so she went to sleep.

Cat was very good at hunting in the dark.
She was never hungry again.
And that's why cats hunt at night and sleep
in the day.

16